Valley
Wisdom

Written by David Orme
Illustrated by Seb Camagajevac

Titles in Full Flight 5

— · — · — · — · — · — · — · — · — · — · — · — · — · — · —

Badger Publishing Limited
15 Wedgwood Gate, Pin Green Industrial Estate,
Stevenage, Hertfordshire SG1 4SU
Telephone: 01438 356907. Fax: 01438 747015
www.badger-publishing.co.uk
enquiries@badger-publishing.co.uk

Valley of Wisdom   ISBN 978 1 84691 120 0

Series Editor: Jonny Zucker
Publisher: David Jamieson
Commissioning Editor: Carrie Lewis
Editor: Paul Martin
Design: Fiona Grant
Illustration: Seb Camagajevac (Beehive Illustration)

Printed in China through Colorcraft Ltd., Hong Kong

Valley of Wisdom

How to use this book

In this book, YOU are the hero.
DO NOT read through from page to page!

You must choose your own path - but choose wisely or you will face great danger!

Turn over this page and begin with part 1.

Follow the 'Go to' prompts when you have chosen your path.

Good luck!

➜ 1 You are an explorer, deep in the rain forests of South America. You are searching for the lost Valley of Wisdom.

At last you find a narrow mountain pass. You scramble through and find you are in the lost valley you have been looking for. But there is a sudden earthquake and the narrow pass behind you is blocked by fallen rocks.

You are trapped in the lost valley. Your only hope of escape is to find the Wisdom of the Ancients! A narrow track disappears into the rainforest. Bravely, you set off...

Go to 2

→2 You reach a junction. From here, tracks go east, south and west.

In the centre of the crossroads, you find three things:

✳ A gold coin.
✳ A wooden stick with a silver top.
✳ A set of tennis rackets.

These objects will help you, but you can only take two of them.

Choose your objects and make a note of them. If you return here, you can change your objects if you wish.

Now choose your route.

West towards the valley entrance.
Go to 18
South towards the sound of water.
Go to 21
East through the dark jungle.
Go to 28

→**3** You are in a room with a chest full of jewels and you fill your bag with as many as you can carry. But was this a good choice? You are still in the valley! Leave the temple and **go to 39.**

→**4** Here there is an old, overgrown road going west and east. A path goes north to the river. Which will you choose?

North to the river? **Go to 38**
East along the old road? **Go to 12**
West along the old road? **Go to 11**

➡5 The path splits again.
Which way this time?

South towards the sound of rushing
water? **Go to 17**
North through a troop of chattering
monkeys? **Go to 31**
East along a path over a grassy plain?
Go to 34

→ 6 You reach the river, but the bridge has been swept away. There is no way to cross. **Go back to 34**

→ 7 It is a long climb. At last you reach the temple of the Ancients. In the great hall, there are three doors. They are labelled:

✳ The secret of TIME.
✳ The secret of WISDOM.
✳ The secret of MONEY.

But you will need a gold coin to open the door of your choice!

No coin? You could:
Start searching the valley again.
Go to 39
Start the adventure again. **Go to 2**

If you have a coin, make your choice now!

Money: **Go to 3**
Time: **Go to 10**
Wisdom: **Go to 27**

➡8 Oh dear! The stick with the silver top belonged to the wise wizards of the forest and the lost tribe really hated them. They think you are a wise wizard. They close in. You are trapped. **Go to 22**

➡9 There is no way out of the clearing: it is a dead end, and we mean DEAD! You have stumbled on the lair of the giant centipedes!

If you have the stick with the silver top, you can beat them back. **Go back to 31**

If not, you have two choices:
Turn and run and hope they can't catch you. **Go to 23**
Try and beat them with one of your tennis rackets if you have them.
Go to 30

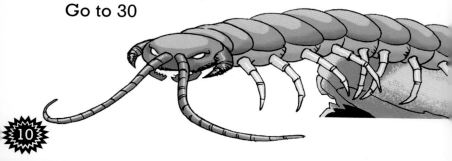

10 You are in a small room. In the centre of the room is a time machine. Bravely, you strap yourself in and switch it on.

The world seems to whizz around you. You close your eyes.

When you open them again, you have moved in space and time. You are back at the narrow mountain pass. It is the day before the earthquake.

Have you been to the room marked 'MONEY'?
Yes? **Go to 40**
No? **Go to 44**

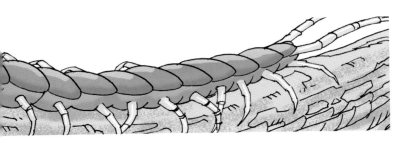

➡ **11** You have now arrived at a clearing in the forest. The clearing is full of dangerous wild cats!

Have you got the silver topped stick with you?
Yes? **Go to 19**
No? **Go to 42**

➡ **12** You reach a place where two paths cross. Which way will you go?

North to the river? **Go to 35**
South along a muddy track? **Go to 29**
West along an old, overgrown road?
Go to 4
East along the old, overgrown road?
Go to 39

➜ **13** The lost tribe who live here hated the wizards who once lived in the forest. They always carried sticks with silver tops. It was a good job you didn't have one! You enjoy a night of feasting. But, the next morning, you must continue your journey.

Will you go…
West? **Go to 28**
East along a rocky valley? **Go to 31**
South along a narrow, secret trail through the jungle? **Go to 26**

➜ **14** You stop for a refreshing drink at the waterfall. Nearby is the lair of a hungry mountain lion – and she is VERY pleased to see you! **Go to 22**

→ 15 You have arrived at a rope bridge across the river. Some of the planks are rotten!

Each plank has a number painted on it.

The wise wizards have set a puzzle to help you cross.

* IF you add two even numbers together, you get an even number.
* IF you add two odd numbers together, you get an .... number.
  Only walk on these planks!

Do you walk on the EVEN numbered planks? **Go to 11**
Do you walk on the ODD numbered planks? **Go to 25**

→ 16 Yellow and blue make green. The purple stones are really slippy. You slip – and the Piranhas are waiting! **Go to 22**

➔ **17** You reach the river. There are two sets of stepping stones to cross. Will you cross on the green stones or the purple stones? There is a riddle painted on a tree to help you.

To find the safest way for you –
be bold, be brave, mix yellow and blue.

So – are you going for:
The green stones? **Go to 12**
The purple stones? **Go to 16**
Try a different route? **Go back to 5**

➔ **18** You have arrived at your starting point, but the pass is still blocked! **Go back to 2**

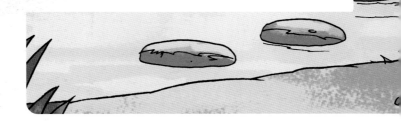

TO FIND
THE
SAFEST
WAY
FOR YOU
BE BOLD,
BE BRAVE,
MIX YELLOW
AND BLUE

➡ **19** Phew! That was lucky!

The wizards used the stick to control the cats. They roll over and you tickle their tummies.

Now choose a route:
West along a path that climbs steeply upwards? **Go to 33**
East along an old, overgrown road? **Go to 4**
North to the river? **Go to 36**

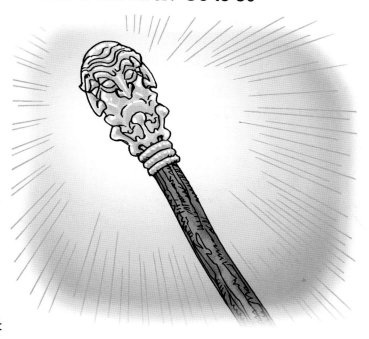

➜**20** You reach the river, but the bridge has been washed away.
Go back to 39

➜**21** You have arrived at the river bank. You climb down some slippery rocks to reach the water. At this point, the river goes underground on its way out of the lost valley.

Could this be a way of escape?
What do you decide?
Dive in the river? **Go to 32**
Go back? **Go to 2**

➜**22** Looks like you have come to a terrible end! Try again? **Go to 1**

➜23 Smart move. The centipedes are very slow! **Go to 31**

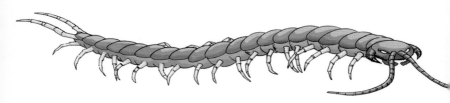

➜24 You are in a room with a chest full of jewels and you fill your bag with as many as you can carry.

Now what do you want to do?
Go back into the lost valley with your treasure? **Go to 39**
Try the door labelled time? **Go to 10**

➜25 That was a really rotten choice! Two odd numbers always make an even one! The planks crumble under you - and the river is full of hungry killer fish! **Go to 22**

➜26 At last you reach the river bank. A small boat is waiting, with a ferryman sitting in it.

He will row you across the river, but only if you give him a gold coin. If you have one, go across the river with the ferryman, then **walk to 4**.

If you don't, you only have one choice: head back to the village and turn east along the rocky valley. **Go to 31**

➜27 This was a wise choice.

The room is empty, but there are two doors leading out of it. One is labelled 'MONEY' and the other 'TIME'. Both doors have keys in them. Which will you try first?

Money? **Go to 24**
Time? **Go to 10**

➜28 The path through the forest splits at a spring of fresh water. You have a cool drink, then decide where to go from here.

One route heads east. The sound of drums is coming from this direction. One route goes south and you hear the faint sound of rushing water. One route goes west through the dark jungle.

Which will you choose?
East? **Go to 37**
South? **Go to 15**
West? **Go to 2**

➜29 You are in a huge swamp!
You find you are slowly sinking into
quicksand.

If you have the tennis rackets with you,
you can strap them on your feet to stop
yourself sinking. **Go to 39**

Don't have them? **Go to 22**

➜30 You put up a good fight, but the
centipedes get you and inject you with
deadly venom. You cannot move. Soon,
they will eat you alive… **Go to 22**

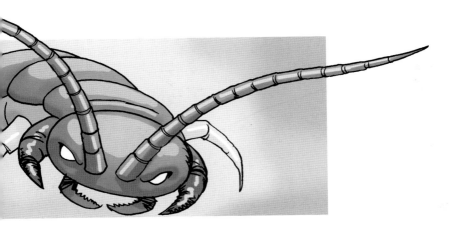

➜31 You are at a place where three tracks meet. Which way will you choose?

North into a jungle clearing? **Go to 9**
South through a troop of chattering monkeys? **Go to 5**
West along a rocky valley? **Go to 37**

→ 32 Sorry – bad idea! The river travels for miles underground and you can't hold your breath that long!

Go to 22

→ 33 This path takes you to a tall mountain cliff. There is no way out of the valley here.

Go back to 11

→ 34 Here a mighty tree grows in the middle of a grassy plain. To the east is a rocky wall with a waterfall tumbling down it. The path splits. Which way will you go?

Towards the waterfall? **Go to 14**
West into the jungle? **Go to 5**
South to the river? **Go to 6**

35 You reach the river. There are two sets of stepping stones to cross. Will you cross on the green stones or the purple stones? There is a riddle painted on a tree to help you.

To find the safest way for you —
be bold, be brave, mix yellow and blue.

So – are you going for:
The green stones? **Go to 43**
The purple stones? **Go to 16**
Try a different route? **Go back to 12**

➔36 You have arrived at a rope bridge across the river. Some of the planks are rotten! Each plank has a number painted on them.

The wizards of old have set a puzzle to help you cross.
* **IF you add two even numbers together, you get an even number.**
* **IF you add two odd numbers together, you get an .... number.**
  Only walk on these planks!

Do you walk on the EVEN numbered planks? **Go to 41**
Do you walk on the ODD numbered planks? **Go to 25**

➡ 37 You have reached the village of the lost tribe. They all rush out of their huts when you arrive.

Have you got the stick with the silver top?

Yes? **Go to 8**
No? **Go to 13**

➡ 38 At last you reach the river bank. A small boat is waiting, with a ferryman sitting in it. He will row you across the river, but only if you give him a gold coin.

If you have one, you will be able to reach the village of the lost tribe.
Go to 37

If you don't, or if you decide not to go to the village, **go back to 4.**

→ 39 You are at the foot of a tall cliff. Paths go north, west and south. To the east there is a great gateway. Through the gateway, a crumbling flight of steps climbs the cliffs.

Which way will you go?
North to the river bank? **Go to 20**
West along an old, overgrown road?
Go to 12
South along the bank of a stream?
Go to 29
Up the steps? **Go to 7**

➜40 Congratulations! You can leave the valley and live a life of luxury. Your quest is over.

➜41 A good choice! You cross the bridge safely and walk through the jungle. **Go to 28**

➜42 You have no means to control the cats – and they are very hungry!

Go to 22

➜43 You cross the river safely. You are now on the north bank. **Walk on to 5**

➜44 You are free from the valley but have no treasure to show for your adventure. But you have learnt many secrets about the valley, so why not try again?

Up for it? **Go to 2**

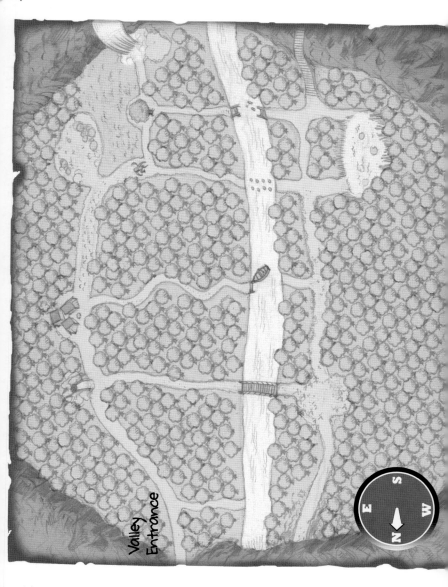

Valley
Entrance